Name

_____

Contact

_____

_____

_____

KEY

• Task		
✕ Completed		
❯ Migrated		
❮ Scheduled		
— Note		
◯ Event		
~~Irrelevant~~		
✳ Priority Signifier		
Connect the dots to make your own Bullets and Signifiers		

For more information, go to page 239.

LEUCHTTURM1917

Getting started

To get the most out of your Bullet Journal, please read the instructions at the back of this book and watch the videos featured on bulletjournal.com.

Do what works for you

These instructions give you a basic framework of core methods to get you started. If a certain technique isn't working for you, feel free to modify it so that it does.

Less is more

Though you're highly encouraged to customize your Bullet Journal, it's best to keep it simple. Use the absolute minimum amount of effort and methods to stay productive.

Review... and review again

Even if it's just five minutes a day, review your Bullet Journal before you get started in the morning and before you go to sleep at night. This helps you fill in any gaps and stay mindful of your time.

INDEX

INDEX

INDEX

INDEX

FUTURE LOG

FUTURE LOG

FUTURE LOG

INTRODUCTION

You hold in your hands the Bullet Journal, a totally customizable (and totally forgiving) organization system that adapts to your needs. It's modular by design, and comprised of interchangeable methods that help you quickly capture and organize information. The Bullet Journal can be your to-do list, sketchbook, notebook, and diary, but most likely, it will be all of the above.

Four key concepts lay the foundation of the Bullet Journal: Rapid Logging, Collections, Migration, and Indexing.

RAPID LOGGING

Note-taking and traditional journaling take time; the more complex the entry, the more effort is expended. The more effort expended, the more of a chore it becomes, the more likely you'll underutilize or abandon your journal. Rapid Logging is the solution.

Rapid Logging relies on the use of short-form notation, or Bullets. Bullets are short, objective sentences that allow you to quickly log entries into your Bullet Journal. To help organize your entries, they are divided into three categories: Tasks, Events, and Notes.

The Task Bullet

Tasks are represented by the dot '•' bullet and indicate actionable items (e.g. "pick up dry cleaning"). There are four main Task states:

Task.

Migrated Task: items that have been moved to the following month or to a Collection.

Scheduled Task: tasks with specific dates in upcoming months. Can be added to your Future Log.

Completed Task.

Some Tasks require multiple steps to complete. These steps—Subtasks—can be listed by simply indenting new Task Bullets underneath the original Master Task. Master Tasks can only be marked as complete once all the Subtasks have been completed or marked irrelevant.

Ọ The Event Bullet

Events are represented by an "O" bullet. Events are date-related entries that can either be scheduled (e.g. "Charlie's birthday") or logged after they occur (e.g. "signed the lease"). Tasks that are recorded after they've been completed should also be logged as Events (e.g. "bought plane tickets"). Events that need to be scheduled on a specific date that fall outside of the current month are added to the Future Log.

Event entries, no matter how personal or emotionally taxing, should be as objective and brief as possible when Rapid Logging. The Event "movie night" bears no more or less weight than "best friend moves to Boston." That being said, once you've rapid logged an Event, feel free to write about it at length on the next available page.

⁝ The Note Bullet

Notes are represented with a dash "–". Notes include facts, ideas, thoughts, and observations. Notes are entries that you want to remember, but aren't immediately or necessarily actionable. This Bullet works well for meeting, lecture, or classroom notes.

Create Signifiers

Signifiers are symbols that give your Bullets additional context. A handful of useful examples are listed here; feel free to come up with your own as you get more comfortable.

Priority
Represented by "*"; used to give a Task priority. Placed to the left of a Bullet so that you can quickly scan your pages to find the most important entries.

Explore
Represented by an eye; used when there is something that requires further research, information, or discovery.

Inspiration
Represented by an exclamation point; most commonly paired with a Note. Great ideas, personal mantras, and genius insights will never be misplaced again!

 Build your own Bullets.

Bullet types and Signifiers can easily adapt to your needs, and you can use the mini-grids found in the key of this book to help you design your own. For example, people who like to schedule events in advance—specifically ones that require their attendance—can use the Appointment Bullet listed below:

The Appointment Bullet.

 The Appointment complete.

COLLECTIONS

Collections serve to group and organize your entries. They can be used for anything from shopping lists to meeting notes to personal goals. Creating a Collection is simple: all you need to do is give a blank page a topic. There are three core Collection types: the Monthly Log, the Daily Log, and the Future Log.

The Monthly Log

The Monthly Log helps you organize—you guessed it—your month. It consists of a calendar and a task list. To set up your first Monthly Log, go to the next available spread of facing pages. The left page will be your Calendar Page; the right will be your Task Page.

The Calendar gives you a birdseye view of the month. To set it up: title the page with the current month's name. Now list all the dates of that month down the left margin, followed by the first letter of the corresponding day. Monday the 14th would be "14M." Leave some room in the left margin of the page to add Signifiers.

You can use the Calendar Page to record and/or schedule Events and Tasks. Just keep the entries as short as possible, as this page is designed to provide a quick birdseye view.

The Task Page is a list of both Tasks that you want to tend to that month, and unfinished Tasks that have migrated from the previous month.

Tips

Set up the next Monthly Log at the end of the current month, and not way ahead of time. You never know how many pages you may use in any given month.

Use a timeframe that works best for you. Some Bullet Journalers also create a Weekly Log, in which they migrate items from the previous week to keep it fresh in their minds.

The Daily Log

The Daily Log is designed for day-to-day use. At the top of the page, record the date as your topic. Throughout the course of the day, simply Rapid Log your Tasks, Events, and Notes as they occur. If you don't fill a page, add the next date wherever you left off and you're ready to continue.

Tips

Don't set up Daily Logs way ahead of time. Create them as you go or the night before. You never know how much space you may need on any given day.

The Future Log

This Collection is used to store items that either need to be scheduled months in advance…or things that you want to get around to someday. Set up your Future Log by dividing your pages into months. For example, two equally-spaced horizontal lines across facing pages create a six-month calendar.

Tips

Save one Future Log page so that it can be used for unscheduled future Tasks like goals (e.g. paint the house).

You can find a variety of alternate methods to help you format and organize your Future Log on bulletjournal.com. Pick one that speaks to you.

MIGRATION

Migrating content is a cornerstone of the Bullet Journal. Once you've hit your second month of journaling, take a glance at your previous entries. See any unresolved Tasks? "X" out your completed Tasks and assess whether the remaining open Tasks are still relevant.

If a Task has become irrelevant, strike out the whole line, including the Task Bullet. If the Task still needs your attention, migrate it: turn the "•" into ">" to signify that you've migrated that Task, then add it to the Task Page of your new Monthly Log.

You also have the option of Migrating scheduled Tasks and Events. When you're setting up a new month, migrate any entries scheduled for that month from your Future Log into your new Monthly Log. Scheduled items are placed on the Monthly Log's Calendar Page.

It may seem like a lot of effort to have to rewrite items over and over, but that's intentional. This process makes you pause and consider each item. If an entry isn't even worth the effort to rewrite it, then it's probably not that important. Get rid of it.

The purpose of Migrating is to distill the things that are truly worth the effort, to become aware of our own patterns and habits, and to separate the signal from the noise.

INDEXING

The first few pages of this book are your Index. The Index is where the Bullet Journal really comes together. As you start to use your book, simply add the topics of your Collections and their page numbers to the Index, so you can quickly find and reference them at any point.

Collections that span a series of consecutive spreads are indexed as such: "Topic Name: 5-10."

Some Collections are recurring and can be spread throughout your Bullet Journal. These topics can be indexed as such: "Topic Name: 5–10, 23, 34–39, …"

The Index can also be used to group other types of entries. For example, if you use your notebook to draw, create an entry called "drawings" in your Index, followed by the corresponding page numbers.

Why Bullet Journal?

Time is the most precious resource we have. Bullet Journaling is only partially about getting organized. The real goal is to develop a mindful practice that helps you identify and focus on the things that are truly worth your time.

For more tips, tricks, and methods: bulletjournal.com

BULLETJOURNAL.COM

The Bullet Journal is supported by a very active community that contributes to the evolution of the system. The instructions included in this book are the most basic constellation of methods. To see variations and alternate methods, tips and tricks, or to contribute your own, please visit bulletjournal.com.

LEUCHTTURM1917
LEUCHTTURM ALBENVERLAG GMBH & CO. KG
21495 Geesthacht · Deutschland · Germany
Made in China · Designed in Germany
More information: **www.leuchtturm1917.com**